COULD YOU BE

A MONSTER WAVE
SURFER?

MATT DOEDEN

Raintree is an imprint of Capstone Global Library Limited, a company incorporated in England and Wales having its registered office at 264 Banbury Road, Oxford, OX2 7DY – Registered company number: 6695582

www.raintree.co.uk
myorders@raintree.co.uk

Edited by Michelle Parkin
Designed by Brann Garvey
Original illustrations © Capstone Global Library Limited 2022
Picture research by Eric Gohl
Production by Tori Abraham
Originated by Capstone Global Library Ltd

ISBN 978 1 3982 0574 1

British Library Cataloguing in Publication Data
A full catalogue record for this book is available from the British Library.

Acknowledgements
We would like to thank the following for permission to reproduce photographs: Alamy: Cannon Photography LLC, cover, 1, 4–5, Cavan, 95, Photo Resource Hawaii, 33; AP Images: Red Bull, 58; Getty Images: Brian Bielmann, 108, Leisa Tyler, 70, Richard Hallman, 107, Stringer/AFP, 106, The Mercury News/MediaNews Group, 100; iStockphoto: EpicStockMedia, 6, franckreporter, 79, Richinpit, 97, Simone Tognon, 21; Newscom: ZUMA Press/Richard Hallman, 103; Shutterstock: Angelo DeVal, 49, Gustavo Miguel Fernandes, 69, Jarvis Gray, 17, 75, Joel Everard, 83, mimagephotography, 29, Phillip B. Espinasse, 10, Ramon Carretero, 87, trabantos, 45, 61, Valeria Venezia, 13, Vitor Miranda, 40, Wirestock Images, 55, Wonderful Nature, 99

Printed and bound in India

CONTENTS

ABOUT YOUR ADVENTURE

You cling to your surfboard. Huge waves wash in from the ocean behind you. That's when you see it – a monster wave. Can you catch it? Can you ride it? Should you even try?

Grab your board and hit the beach. Your choices will guide the story. Could you be a monster wave surfer?

Chapter One sets the scene. Then you choose which path to read. Follow the directions at the bottom of the page as you read the stories. The decisions you make will change your outcome. After you finish one path, go back and read the others for new perspectives and more adventures.

CHAPTER 1

SURF'S UP

The waves crash like thunder as they slam onto the shore. The sun shines brightly, reflecting off the crystal blue water. The air smells damp and salty. Sea birds circle overhead, searching for food. The perfect swell rises up behind you.

"It's gonna be the wave of the day!" you shout to your friends.

You've always loved surfing. But you've never surfed such big waves before. They form long, towering tubes of water as they rush to the shore. One mistake on a wave like this could spell disaster. But you're confident. You're ready. You paddle your board to pick up speed. As the wave begins to sweep you up, you pop up onto the board, quickly finding your balance.

The wave carries you along. As you get closer and closer to shore, the top of the wave begins to break. The salty water sprays your face as you crouch down on your board. The giant tube of water surrounds you, but you don't stop. You can't.

You can feel the wave towering over you, ready to crash down on top of you. All you can do is try to stay ahead of the frothy whitewater.

This is the moment. This is your monster wave. Are you up to the challenge?

TO SURF HAWAII'S FAMOUS PIPELINE, TURN TO PAGE 11.

TO HEAD TO NAZARÉ, PORTUGAL, AND ITS RECORD-SETTING WAVES, TURN TO PAGE 41.

TO BRAVE THE SHARK-INFESTED WATERS OF SHIPSTERN BLUFF, TASMANIA, TURN TO PAGE 71.

CHAPTER 2

THE PIPELINE

"Hey!" calls a voice.

You turn to see a curly-haired teenager walking towards you. You're standing on the legendary Ehukai Beach, along the north shore of the Hawaiian island of Oahu. The sand is warm and the sun is shining.

You're soaking in the sun near Hawaii's Banzai Pipeline. It's one of the most famous surfing spots in the world. Surfers from all over travel to Hawaii for a chance to ride the monster wave. But Pipeline is not for novices. Breaks can drop surfers onto the shallow reef under the surface. Hundreds have been injured or died because of the heavy, giant wave.

TURN THE PAGE.

"What's up?" you say as he approaches. You can tell by the teen's tanned skin that he spends his share of time at the beach.

"You looked good out there," he says. "I was watching you on that last wave."

You wince. You wiped out on the last wave. You hoped that nobody had noticed.

"No, I'm serious," he continues. "I know it didn't end well, but your control before that was pretty good. You're new here, right?"

You shrug. "I've been surfing for a few years. But the waves are much smaller back home. They're nothing like Pipeline."

Your family had planned this holiday for a year. Ever since you found out you were coming to Hawaii, you've been focused on surfing its famous Pipeline. You've spent every spare moment practising.

So far, you've been taking it slow. You haven't ventured into the biggest waves yet, preferring to stick to spots where the surfing is a bit less extreme. But you're working up your nerve to try Pipeline.

"I'm Kai," he says, extending his hand. You shake it and introduce yourself. "I think you've got a real knack for surfing. I know a lot of people who have been surfing for years and wouldn't ride out those waves like you just did."

"Thanks," you say, taking a deep breath.

At first you were worried that Kai was going to make fun of you. But now you can tell that he really means it. You try not to show how much it means to you to hear his kind words.

"I'm about to head out to catch a few waves myself. Want to join me?" Kai asks.

Your parents want you back at your hotel room by supper time. A quick glance at your watch shows that you've got less than an hour. They'll be upset if you're late. But something about Kai really makes you want to get out there.

TO JOIN KAI, TURN TO PAGE 16.
TO SUGGEST MEETING UP TOMORROW INSTEAD, TURN TO PAGE 18.

"I'd love to, Kai, but I need to get back to my hotel," you say. "Will you be out here tomorrow?"

Kai shrugs. "Might be. Depends on the conditions. If the barrels are like they are today, I'll probably be out."

With that, you say goodbye. You flop down on the sand and take in the view. You can tell why many people call Pipeline the best surfing in the world. The waves roll in beautifully, with long, perfectly formed barrels. You watch other surfers pulling in and out, turning and throwing spray from their boards, and occasionally wiping out. You're glad you're not the only one.

You keep an eye on Kai, who has paddled out on his bright yellow board. He's bobbing up and down out beyond the reef, where the waves break. Finally, he spots his wave. He's really good. You marvel at how easily he controls his board as he slides along.

But when Kai enters the barrel, it all goes wrong. The board suddenly kicks out from under him and he is sent sprawling into the water. You wait for him to resurface. A few seconds pass. Then a few more. You still don't see him.

You stand up, squinting as you scan the water. Kai's yellow board is washing onto the beach, but you still don't see Kai. Your heart begins to race. You look around. Nobody else seems to be paying attention.

TO CALL FOR HELP, TURN TO PAGE 25.
TO RUSH OUT INTO THE WATER, TURN TO PAGE 28.

With that, Kai's gone. As you stand there, watching the waves roll in, his words echo over and over in your mind.

Stick to more beginner-type waves, you think. Kai may have been right, but it stings you.

TO TRY ONE MORE TIME ON YOUR OWN, TURN TO PAGE 27.
TO GIVE UP, TURN TO PAGE 34.

You're too late. You won't be able to pick up the speed you need to catch this wave. So you wait. It doesn't take long before another swell rolls in. This time you're ready for it. As the wave sweeps you along, you spring to your feet. You quickly find your balance near the centre of the board.

You ride along the wall of wave as the barrel begins to form. The long, curling tube is like a tunnel in the water.

Here goes nothing, you think.

You dart down into the barrel. For several seconds, you hold your own, battling the powerful, surging water. Then the nose of your board kicks away from you. You fall into the whitewater. You hit the water hard, but quickly recover. The leash on your ankle keeps your board close.

TURN THE PAGE.

With the wave's energy spent, you hop back on and paddle to shore.

"Awesome!" Kai shouts, giving you a high-five.

"Thanks," you reply. "Just wish I hadn't wiped out there at the end."

Kai shakes his head. "Don't be silly, you did well."

You glance at your watch. It's time to go. You're already going to be a few minutes late. Luckily, your parents are running late too. You spend a relaxing evening together, your thoughts never far from Pipeline. You're proud of yourself, but you really wish you'd made that wave barrel.

TO TRY AGAIN TOMORROW, TURN TO PAGE 37.

TO BE SATISFIED THAT YOU SURFED ONE OF THE WORLD'S BIGGEST WAVES, TURN TO PAGE 39.

"Help!" You call, pointing at the water. "Someone is in trouble!"

Up and down the beach, heads turn in your direction. Two young women spring into action.

"I see him!" one of them shouts.

The women hurry into the water and swim out to retrieve Kai. You look on as they carry him to shore and do CPR. You sigh with relief as Kai regains consciousness and coughs up loads of seawater. He's going to be alright.

You return to your hotel room, shaken by what you've seen. For the rest of the night, you're distracted.

If a surfer as experienced as Kai can have such a close call on Pipeline, do I have any business surfing it? you think.

TURN THE PAGE.

You barely sleep as the images play again and again in your mind. When morning comes, your mum asks if you want to go sightseeing. You had planned to head back to the beach, but now you're not so sure.

TO HEAD BACK TO THE BEACH FOR MORE SURFING, GO TO PAGE 27.
TO GO WITH YOUR FAMILY, TURN TO PAGE 32.

There's only one thing you can do to get over your fear. You've got to get back out there. And this time, you're going for the big wave. You're going to surf the heart of Pipeline.

With your surfboard tucked under your arm, you head off to the beach. It's early, and the beach is mostly empty. That's fine with you. That way, nobody can laugh at you if you wipe out.

The water feels cool as you wade in. You paddle out beyond the break. The sound of the crashing waves all around fills you with a nervous excitement.

Are you sure you're ready for this? Pipeline tests even the strongest surfers. You do well on smaller waves, but can you tame this monster? Is it really worth the risk?

TO BACK OUT AND SEARCH FOR SMALLER, SAFER WAVES, TURN TO PAGE 34.
TO GO FOR IT, TURN TO PAGE 35.

The waves are merciless. As you drag yourself to shore, they continue to pound you. Finally, you pull yourself onto the wet sand, collapsing with exhaustion.

You lie there for a moment. You're dizzy from the loss of blood. You're panicked and confused. Luckily, an elderly couple spots you as they take a morning walk.

"My friend ... he's out there," you stammer, pointing back to the water.

Your head is swimming, and you're having a hard time collecting your thoughts. The woman tightly wraps her jumper around your leg to stop the bleeding as the man calls for an ambulance.

You're going to be alright. The leg will need a lot of stitches, and you'll be limping for months. But that's not what bothers you. The image of Kai going down at Pipeline will haunt you forever. You'll always wonder if you could have done more.

THE END

TO FOLLOW ANOTHER PATH, TURN TO PAGE 9.

Are you crazy? you think.

You shake your head for even thinking about trying to surf Pipeline. People *die* out there. Do you really want to risk being one of them?

Of course not. There are perfectly good waves further down the beach. Waves that won't kill you.

You're no monster wave surfer. You realize that now. One day, you may regret not trying. But for now, it's better to be safe than sorry.

THE END

TO FOLLOW ANOTHER PATH, TURN TO PAGE 9.

If you don't do this now, you never will. So you lie down on your board and begin to paddle. A large swell builds up behind you. It looks like it's going to be a big wave. This is it!

As you continue to paddle, the wave carries you along. Everything happens quickly. Almost as soon as you're on your feet, the wave hits the reef. It gets steeper and steeper. When it starts to break, you're not quite ready for it. You search for the tube-shaped barrel that makes Pipeline famous. But in your rush, you lose your footing. Your board kicks out from under your feet. You're falling!

Normally, that's not a big deal. But Pipeline sweeps over a very shallow reef. As you fall, the wave drives you head-first into the water and down to the reef below.

TURN THE PAGE.

You don't feel a thing. The crashing waves pound down on your motionless body. Even if someone does come to your rescue, it will be too late. You took on Pipeline, and you lost.

THE END

TO FOLLOW ANOTHER PATH, TURN TO PAGE 9.

You're back out on the beach early the next morning. The Hawaiian sun hasn't had a chance to warm the air yet, but you're ready to go. Yesterday was great, but you know that you can do better.

The water laps against your legs as you wade in. The waves are breaking beautifully – maybe even better than yesterday. All you can think about is riding one of those barrels. You picture sliding your surfboard up and down that perfect wall of water.

Eager, you catch the first wave that comes your way. It's a monster. You take off on the shoulder of the wave. You feel a rush of excitement. Now that you've done this, you're feeling confident. This time, you're not going to settle for the safe ride. You're going in.

TURN THE PAGE.

The barrel takes shape, and you don't hesitate. You duck in, crouching on your board as the water curls overhead. It's perfect!

That's when the wave begins to fall apart. You're trapped inside the barrel as it crumbles, and the weight of the wave crashes down on you. The water slams you down hard on your board.

Luckily, you manage to resurface and slink back to shore. You're bleeding and dizzy. Your legs feel like jelly. You try to stand up, but you fall onto the sand.

You lie there and close your eyes. That was an epic fail. You should have quit when you were ahead. The beach is empty now, but someone will come along soon. All you can do is wait, feeling foolish for thinking you could tame Pipeline all by yourself.

THE END

TO FOLLOW ANOTHER PATH, TURN TO PAGE 9.

Well, it wasn't a perfect run. But you've done something that few surfers in the world have accomplished. You've surfed the Banzai Pipeline.

Now, it's time to turn your attention to other things. You spend the rest of your trip seeing the sights of Oahu. You sample local foods at a lavish *luau*. You go snorkelling at Lanikai Beach. And you even do a little more surfing. But your time on Pipeline is over. It's an experience that you'll never forget.

THE END

TO FOLLOW ANOTHER PATH, TURN TO PAGE 9.

"I'm Rodrigo," he says. "And unless you two are pro surfers, don't even think about going out there today. Or any day, really. But especially today. The swells have to be at least 18 metres. Have you surfed waves like that before?"

You shrug and shake your head. "No. Probably not even half that," you admit. "But we're only here for a couple of days, and we've been dying to try out this area."

It's true. You've dreamed of surfing Nazaré ever since you saw a video of Garrett McNamara online. He set a world record by surfing a 23-metre wave here.

Rodrigo shakes his head. "Yeah, we've been getting a lot more tourists since McNamara's record. Everyone wants to try the big waves. Look, at least wait until tomorrow. Conditions should be better then. At least a little."

You look at Luisa. She may seem shy, but of the two of you, she's the real daredevil. You've never seen a wave she couldn't tame. You can tell she's just itching to get out on the water.

"Tell you what," Rodrigo says. "I'll be out with a friend tomorrow morning. Join us. I can show you the best spots. The *safest* spots. Maybe you won't catch a record wave there, but they'll be big enough. And you can tell all your friends that you surfed Nazaré. What do you say?"

You hate to waste a day when you have so little time to spend here. And you're never going to set any records by waiting for calmer conditions. But maybe Rodrigo is right. Maybe record-setting waves aren't what's important. Maybe you should play it a bit safer.

TO ACCEPT RODRIGO'S OFFER, TURN TO PAGE 44.
TO DECLINE AND TRY TO CATCH A REAL MONSTER, TURN TO PAGE 48.

You meet Rodrigo and his friend Maria near the lighthouse that overlooks the ocean.

Maria greets you with a warm "Hello", but speaks only a few words of English.

"Vamos lá," she says. You know what that means. *Let's go.*

Rodrigo leads the four of you to his jeep. You load up your gear and hop in. It's a short drive to a small, sandy beach with beautiful 7-metre waves breaking. There's not another soul in sight.

As you unload your favourite short board, Maria puts a hand on your arm. She points to another board, a bright yellow big wave board that towers over you. She says something in Portuguese that you don't understand. But her meaning is clear. She wants you to use this board instead.

You hesitate. You haven't done much surfing with a big wave board. You learnt on a short board and like how easy it is to manoeuvre in the water. Yes, big wave boards allow you to paddle into larger waves. But they are harder to control in tight barrels.

TO STICK WITH YOUR TRUSTY SHORT BOARD, TURN TO PAGE 51.
TO TRY MARIA'S BIG WAVE BOARD, TURN TO PAGE 52.

Even out here, where the deeper water absorbs most of the wave's energy, you can feel the power of the swells as you ride up and down. Watching the waves rise up in front of you, you start to have second thoughts. Before, surfing monster waves seemed like an awesome adventure. But now that you're here, you're not sure this was the right choice at all. Are you sure you're ready for this?

TO TRY TO CATCH A WAVE, TURN TO PAGE 54.
TO CALL OFF THE WHOLE IDEA, TURN TO PAGE 66.

You give Maria a smile but shake your head. She shrugs and leans the big wave board against the jeep. With your short board tucked under your arm, you follow Rodrigo out into the water.

You paddle up and over the waves as you get out beyond the break. Once you hit deeper water, the ocean settles. The waves come in as large bumps. They don't take on their familiar breaking shape until they hit the shallower water ahead.

Soon, all four of you are waiting. Luisa floats a few metres from your left. Rodrigo and Maria are scanning the incoming waves on your right.

You see one coming in. Is it a good one? You're not sure. Rodrigo and Maria don't seem to pay the wave any attention. But you're eager to get started.

TO KEEP WATCHING, TURN TO PAGE 56.
TO CATCH THIS WAVE, TURN TO PAGE 57.

Maria has been surfing here for most of her life. If she says a big wave board will work better, you're going to take her advice. You tuck the new board under your arm and carry it out into the water. Rodrigo is already paddling out into the surf. You're quick to follow. Luisa and Maria aren't far behind.

The power of the waves here is equally terrifying and thrilling. As you paddle out past the break, your heart is racing. Rodrigo watches the incoming waves carefully, looking for the right one. When he sees it, he springs into action, paddling his board forwards. As the next wave rolls in behind it, you don't hesitate. You're right behind Rodrigo, building up speed before the wave catches you.

The powerful swell sweeps you along as you spring to your feet. The wave grows steeper and steeper as it hits the shallow water. It feels like you're riding on a wall of water.

As it begins to break, it's like nothing else in the world exists. It's just you and the wave.

You charge into the tube-shaped barrel of the wave. It's like entering a cave made of water. Maria's board is sturdy under your feet. You're glad you decided to take her advice. You can't turn like you do on your short board. But right now, that doesn't really matter.

Finally, the barrel begins to collapse. You could hold on for a few more seconds. But since you don't know these waters well, it might be best to drop out now.

TO DROP OUT AND CATCH THE NEXT WAVE, TURN TO PAGE 62.
TO TRY TO RIDE THIS WAVE AS LONG AS POSSIBLE, TURN TO PAGE 63.

You resist the temptation to ride the first wave that comes your way. And it's a good thing. As the next one rolls in, you can tell that it's going to be a lot bigger. You start paddling to build up speed. The swell begins to grow as it approaches you. You can feel its power as it pulls you along.

You spring to your feet as the swell towers up behind you. The top of the wave begins to break, sending frothy whitewater out in front of it. Your short board is light and agile. You cut and carve your way towards the forming barrel. It's enormous!

You guide your board into the tube. Water sprays all around you. It's by far the biggest wave you have ever surfed.

TO TRY A TRICK, TURN TO PAGE 64.
TO KEEP RIDING THE TUBE, TURN TO PAGE 65.

"Let's do it!" you shout to Luisa. She nods in agreement.

Luisa drops in first, allowing the wave to sweep her along. A second swell follows close behind, and you're ready for it. You align your board towards the shore and start to paddle. As the wave catches up to you, you quickly snap up to your feet. The power of the wave pushes you along. Within seconds, it starts to grow taller and begins to break.

You watch ahead as Luisa ducks into the barrel of her wave. The spray of saltwater stings your face as you charge into yours. But it's all over before it even begins. The wave collapses on itself, dumping you into the water. Luisa suffers a similar fate. Neither of your waves panned out.

TURN THE PAGE.

It's been the greatest wave of your life, but it's time to kick out. You bail out into the breaking surf, dipping beneath the wave as it passes over you. You resurface with a giant smile.

"Woo hoo!" you hear down the shore.

It's Luisa. She's just surfaced from her ride, and you can hear the pure joy in her voice. You paddle over to her and celebrate what you've just done.

"Come on," she urges. "Let's catch another one!"

You ride one monster after another. When storm clouds roll in, you don't even mind. You load up Rodrigo's jeep and go to town. You spend the rest of the day with your new friends, eating, laughing and remembering the greatest surfing day of your life.

THE END

TO FOLLOW ANOTHER PATH, TURN TO PAGE 9.

Just a few seconds more, you think.

The feeling of riding such a giant wave is amazing. You can't bear to give up even a second too soon. The wave is falling apart, though, and the most thrilling part of the ride is over.

Just as you decide to bail out, everything changes. Your board smashes into a huge rock. The impact sends you flying into the violently crashing surf. You slam down hard onto the jagged rock. You can feel bones crunching. You can taste the saltwater that rushes into your mouth and lungs as you gasp.

Your consciousness flickers and blinks out. Maybe one of the others saw you hit the rock. Maybe they're rushing to your rescue right now. Or maybe your first monster wave was also your last.

THE END

TO FOLLOW ANOTHER PATH, TURN TO PAGE 9.

The thing you love most about your short board is how easy it is to control. It's made for tricks. As your board cruises along the wall of water, you turn hard so the nose of the board carries you up. Your plan is to get near the top of the wave, then do a quick snap, quickly turning to ride back down the wave. It's a trick you've done hundreds of times.

But you've never done it on a wave like this. As you climb the monster, your speed stalls out. You can't turn around quickly enough. For a moment, you feel like you're floating. But you're really falling. You tumble down the wave, crashing hard into the water. Your board comes down on top of your head and knocks you unconscious.

You never wake up. You tried to surf a monster, but it proved to be too big for you to tame.

THE END

TO FOLLOW ANOTHER PATH, TURN TO PAGE 9.

You can't even think about trying a trick just now. Just staying on your feet is challenging enough. You slide through the tube, crouching low to stay out of the frothy, broken wave. Finally as the wave comes to an end, you bail out. You dip below the surface as the wave passes over you.

You resurface and swim for the shore. In the distance, you watch the others ride their own waves, amazed that you just did the same.

You sit on the wet sand. Luisa, fresh off of her wave, comes to shore and flops down next to you.

"Now that was a wave," she says.

The two of you stand up and head back into the churning water. It's just the beginning of one of the greatest days of your life.

THE END

TO FOLLOW ANOTHER PATH, TURN TO PAGE 9.

Luisa is getting ready to catch the next wave. But you just can't do it. The waves are too big and powerful. One wrong move and you'll be crushed.

"Wait, Luisa!" you shout.

But it's too late. She's already begun to paddle, and she can't hear you over the roar of the ocean. You watch as the wave catches up to her. It carries her along as it begins to make a barrel. Soon Luisa is so far away that you can't even see her.

All alone, you do the only thing you can. You meekly paddle back to shore, steering clear of the fearsome waves.

Maybe monster wave surfing just isn't for you.

THE END

TO FOLLOW ANOTHER PATH, TURN TO PAGE 9.

You can't resist. Nothing beats the thrill of riding inside a barrel. You set yourself up to go inside, ignoring the violently crashing water just a metre from your board.

Inside the barrel, it's like nothing else exists in the world. But quickly, you realize your error. This wave is a monster, and the barrel doesn't hold its shape for long. It's collapsing, and you have no way out.

The force of the water slamming down on top of you is too much to take. It batters your body and knocks you out cold.

Out here, in such violent waters, no one is going to be able to help. The biggest wave of your life is also going to be your last.

THE END

TO FOLLOW ANOTHER PATH, TURN TO PAGE 9.

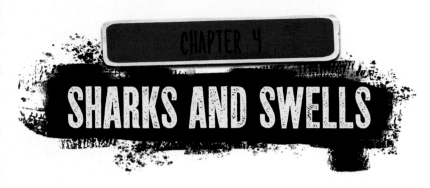

CHAPTER 4

SHARKS AND SWELLS

"Ready to roll?" asks Deshaun.

You give a thumbs up, and he revs the engine on your rented jet ski. You and Deshaun are best friends, and you've surfed many of the most famous surfing spots in the world. But you've never had an adventure quite like this.

Your destination is a surfing spot unlike any other – Shipstern Bluff, located off the southern coast of Tasmania, off Australia. It's so remote that it takes a 29-kilometre jet ski ride over cold, rough seas just to get there.

TURN THE PAGE.

You're no stranger to rough water, but the violent waves here make you wonder if this is worth it. But since you've come this far, there's no turning back now.

Soon, you see the towering, granite bluff rise over the horizon. You know you're close. The waves roll in with shocking violence. Even a pro surfer like you can't help but wonder if this is a good idea.

Deshaun cuts the engine on the jet ski. For a few minutes, you both just stare at the waves, watching them break with terrible force. The waters here are rough and unpredictable. You both try to get a feel for what you can even do out here.

Finally, Deshaun turns to you. He's got that grin on his face that tells you he's about to try something dangerous. "Let's do it," he says. "You –"

"I know, I know," you interrupt. "You only live once," you both say together. This has been Deshaun's motto since you've known him. He's always pushed you to your limits.

This is no ordinary surfing spot. You're not going to be able to just paddle out to catch a wave. Instead, you'll need a tow behind the jet ski to pick up the speed needed to drop in on a wave.

"You wanna go first?" Deshaun asks.

TO TAKE THE FIRST TURN, TURN TO PAGE 74.
TO LET DESHAUN GO FIRST, TURN TO PAGE 77.

You're here to surf. That's what you're going to do.

"Yeah, I'm ready," you answer.

Deshaun smiles and hands you the rope. He starts the motor and pulls away until the rope is tight.

"Hit it!" you shout as you hold on to the handle.

Deshaun revs the jet ski motor and pulls you like a wakeboarder. He steers towards a building wave that's about to start breaking. When you're up to speed, you let go of the rope and turn the board into the wave. It's time to surf.

The cold wind blows spray into your face as you climb the face of the wave. This is no smooth ride. The wave itself is made up of steps, like a staircase. Your board bucks beneath your feet as you go down each step, riding lower and lower.

75

As the wave breaks behind you, the board shudders and kicks. But you hold on.

The wave is breaking hard now. If you keep going, you risk getting thrown off of your board. Or you could bail out. Either way, you're in for a rough ride.

TO PULL IN AND TRY TO STAY ON THE WAVE, TURN TO PAGE 78.
TO BAIL OUT, TURN TO PAGE 80.

"You go first, buddy," you reply.

As your jet ski is tossed and turned in the churning waves, you're not sure you're ready to hop in.

Deshaun holds onto the tow rope. You fire the jet ski motor and drag him behind you. He looks like a wakeboarder, clutching the rope's handle while standing up on his board.

Everywhere you look, waves are forming and breaking just as quickly. Some of them are taller than a house!

You pick up speed. There's a monster wave forming to the right. A smaller one is forming to the left. You know which one Deshaun would choose – the big one. But this is your decision.

TO TOW DESHAUN INTO THE BIG WAVE, TURN TO PAGE 81.
TO HEAD FOR THE SMALLER WAVE, TURN TO PAGE 82.

There's no telling how long this wave will last. You're going to ride it as long as you can. You can feel the force of the water behind you as it surges and churns over the shallow reef below. Suddenly, the wave begins to break rapidly. Whitewater washes over you as you're thrown from your board. You go down hard. The wave passes over you.

For a moment, you can't tell up from down as you struggle to the surface. That's when you realize that you're not alone.

TURN TO PAGE 86.

It's been a very short and very rough ride, but it's time to bail out. Yet that's no easy task. The rough structure of the wave tries to throw you off your board at every step. But you keep your balance. Finally you bail out, diving into the water before the entire wave crashes down on top of you.

"Woo hoo!" you shout as you resurface.

Deshaun is already zipping in on the jet ski. You climb up onto the back and give him a big smile.

"My turn!" Deshaun says.

For the next hour, you take turns riding the wild waves of Shipstern. On your last wave of the day, Deshaun has an idea.

"I dare you to do a trick," he says.

TO TRY THE TRICK, TURN TO PAGE 88.
TO STICK TO A MORE BASIC RIDE, TURN TO PAGE 94.

Deshaun wants to go big, so that's what you do. You hit the throttle and head straight into the big wave. Just as you reach it, you bank hard to the left. Deshaun lets go of the rope as he slingshots into the giant wave.

Even over the crashing surf, you can hear Deshaun whooping and yelling as he turns his way down the wave's steps. He's having the time of his life.

But then, he falls down – hard. You watch for him to surface. But as the first wave passes, a second wave sweeps over the spot where he went down. Seconds pass. You bring the jet ski around, searching the area and shouting out Deshaun's name.

TO DIVE INTO THE WATER TO SEARCH FOR DESHAUN, TURN TO PAGE 84.
TO KEEP LOOKING FROM THE JET SKI, TURN TO PAGE 85.

You play it safe and head for the smaller wave. It's still impressive. Deshaun lets go of the rope and drives down the face of the wave. You can't help but admire his skills. He rides to the top of the wave, then does a quick snap, turning his board back down again. When his ride is over, he's all smiles.

"Next time, go for the big wave," Deshaun teases.

The two of you take turns, surfing one wave after the next. The water is rough. The wipeouts are intense as you struggle to stay above water. But you're getting the hang of it. As your day comes to a close, Deshaun dares you to catch some air on the next wave.

"Imagine if you could do it out here!" he says.

TO TRY THE TRICK, TURN TO PAGE 88.
TO JUST ENJOY YOUR FINAL WAVE, TURN TO PAGE 94.

Panic sets in. You do the only thing you can think of. You dive into the water, desperate to find your friend.

But the moment you jump in, you hear Deshaun yelling. He comes up a metre from the jet ski and quickly pulls himself back on. You jumped in for nothing.

You turn to swim back to the jet ski when an enormous wave breaks right on top of you. The weight and force of it push you under the water. For a moment, you find yourself flailing, fighting the current and trying to get back to the surface.

TURN TO PAGE 86.

Jumping into the water would be foolish. You'd never find your friend in this rough water. Luckily, you don't have to. Deshaun pops up a moment later, gasping for air. He's okay!

"I gotta do that again," he blurts out.

He's not even a little bit spooked by his close encounter with drowning. You, on the other hand, are more terrified than ever. Deshaun pulls himself back onto the jet ski and lets out a deep breath.

"Your turn," he says with a smirk.

TO BACK OUT OF SURFING SHIPSTERN, TURN TO PAGE 93.
TO CATCH A WAVE, TURN TO PAGE 96.

As you continue to struggle to the surface, a long, dark shape swoops in. It's a shark!

It all happens so fast that you can't react. The young great white shark opens its jaws and sinks its teeth into your left leg. Pain shoots up your leg as the powerful animal begins to drag you down.

Your lungs feel about to burst. A red haze of blood begins to cloud the water. You don't have much time left. You have to act now!

TO TRY TO PULL YOUR LEG FREE FROM THE SHARK'S JAWS, TURN TO PAGE 90.
TO USE YOUR OTHER LEG TO KICK THE SHARK'S HEAD, TURN TO PAGE 91.

Deshaun doesn't really think you can do it.

With a grin, you reply, "Watch me."

Luckily, Deshaun tows you into the best wave you've had all day. You ride the monster until it starts to collapse. Just before it does, you quickly turn up towards the lip to launch yourself into the air.

The trick is doomed to fail. You sail up over the lip of the wave and soar through the air for a moment, but the churning water below makes the trick impossible to land. The violent water kicks your board out from under your feet, and you slam into the water head-first. The water here is shallow, and you fall straight into the trough of the wave.

Only a metre of water separates you from the rocky ocean floor. It's not nearly enough.

Your head strikes the rock with terrible force. You lose consciousness immediately. You don't hear Deshaun's frantic cries as he searches for you and drags you from the water. You don't hear or feel anything ever again. You took on Shipstern Bluff, and you lost.

THE END

TO FOLLOW ANOTHER PATH, TURN TO PAGE 9.

You have to get away! You do everything you can to shake your leg free of the shark's jaws. But its grip is far too strong. It won't let go. The shark drags you down deeper towards the ocean floor.

It gives up for a moment, and you try to escape. But as soon as it lets go, the shark's jaws close in on you again. This time, the razor-sharp teeth sink into your shoulder and chest. Bones snap. The water turns pink. The shark strikes again and again, but you don't feel it any more. You've surfed your last wave.

THE END

TO FOLLOW ANOTHER PATH, TURN TO PAGE 9.

The pain sweeps through your body, but you try to stay conscious. The shark has your left leg, but your right leg is still free. In some part of your mind, you remember a video you once saw that said to hit a shark in the nose if it attacks. So you bend your knee, then deliver the hardest kick you can directly to the shark's nose.

Its grip loosens a bit, but the shark doesn't let go. Your lungs are about to burst under the water. You fear you might pass out from the pain. You have just enough energy for one more try. Again, you kick the animal with all the force you can generate.

The shark lets go! You don't waste time. You swim to the surface with everything you have. You gasp for air as you break the surface, then yell for Deshaun. There's no telling when the shark will be back.

TURN THE PAGE.

You're lucky. Deshaun finds you right away. You scramble onto the back of the jet ski. The shark's teeth have shredded your wetsuit and punctured your leg in several places. Blood flows freely from the wounds. But Deshaun knows what to do. He quickly wraps the wound to stop the flow of blood.

"We have to get you back and to the hospital," he says as he revs the motor.

It's going to be a long, painful trip back. But you've survived. And one thing's for sure. You're never coming back to the dangerous Shipstern Bluff.

THE END

TO FOLLOW ANOTHER PATH, TURN TO PAGE 9.

"Sorry man, I just can't do it," you say, as the waves batter the jet ski. "I know you had your heart on both of us surfing Shipstern, but I don't have the nerve."

Deshaun is disappointed. You can see it in his face. But eventually, he just shrugs.

"More surfing for me then," he says.

You spend the next hour towing Deshaun into waves. He's having the time of his life. Then, it's time to head back. It's a long trip back. You wonder if you made the right choice. You had one chance in your life to tame one of surfing's most iconic spots. You hope you don't regret passing it up.

THE END

TO FOLLOW ANOTHER PATH, TURN TO PAGE 9.

You just shake your head. It's going to be your last wave of the day, and you're not going to waste it trying a trick.

Instead, you take one of the most thrilling rides of your life. Deshaun tows you into a huge monster wave. You move up and down the massive wall, riding the wave until you shoot out the other end of the barrel. Amazingly, you manage to stay on your board the whole time. Deshaun is hooting and shouting by the time he picks you up.

"You did it, man," he says, giving you a high-five. "You tamed Shipstern!"

You can't wipe the smile off your face. You know you'll never forget the day you conquered a big one at Shipstern Bluff.

THE END

TO FOLLOW ANOTHER PATH, TURN TO PAGE 9.

You take a deep breath. You'll probably never get another shot at doing this. You're not going to back out now.

"You only live once," you tell Deshaun with a smile.

You grab the rope and hop onto the board. Deshaun guns the motor, almost ripping the rope out of your grasp. But you hold on. It's going to be a wild ride.

Of course, Deshaun heads straight for the biggest wave he can find. It towers over you. You slingshot in and climb the wall of the wave. You're in awe of its power. But you're doing it! To your right, the wave begins to barrel. You quickly pull into the tube-shaped tunnel, crouching low as you ride the barrel.

You can feel the wave about to collapse, so you skilfully guide your board to the bottom of the wave. Then you bail out as gently as possible.

The breaking wave slams into you, but you're ready. As soon as it passes, you're back on the surface of the water. Deshaun is loudly cheering you on.

It was a perfect wave. And even though you catch half a dozen more waves before the day is over, you'll always remember the first one. It is, without a doubt, the greatest moment of your surfing life.

THE END

TO FOLLOW ANOTHER PATH, TURN TO PAGE 9.

CHAPTER 5

BIG-WAVE SURFING

For many, surfing is more than a sport. It's a way of life. The thrill of riding waves, being in touch with nature and spending time with friends keeps people coming back for more.

No one is sure exactly when surfing started. It was part of many ancient Polynesian cultures. Hawaiians took surfing to California in the late 1800s. Soon, surfers flocked to beaches in California and Australia. Films and songs about surfing helped spread the sport's popularity.

By the mid-1900s, surfing was becoming more than just a pastime. It was growing into a competitive sport.

In 1959, the first West Coast Surfing Championships took place in California. Two years later, the United States Surfing Association (USSA) formed. Since then, the best surfers in the world have honed their skills and developed new tricks in a quest to be the best in the world.

Meanwhile, some riders were more interested in riding the biggest waves possible. The sport of big wave surfing grew up on the beaches of Hawaii. Surfing legends such as George Downing, Wally Froiseth, Woody Brown and Buzzy Trent tried to catch the monster waves that were too big for most surfers to even consider riding.

The sport soon spread beyond Hawaii. Surfers sought out monster waves off the coasts of California, Australia, South Africa and more. Many of these spots were hard to reach. Surfers needed watercraft to tow them into the waves.

In 2011, Garrett McNamara made headlines by surfing a 23.77-metre wave in Portugal. Seven years later, Rodrigo Koxa broke that record. Koxa's wave measured a stunning 24.38-metre high.

Some of the best big wave surfers compete in the World Surf League (WSL) Big Wave World Tour. This series of events started in 2014.

Big wave surfing may be thrilling, but it is also a highly dangerous sport. Massive waves can push surfers down deep under the water. Since waves break on shallow reefs, surfers run the risk of slamming into the ocean floor, which may be covered in sharp rocks. A blow to the head can quickly become deadly. In some places, such as Shipstern Bluff, Tasmania, and Half Moon Bay, California, surfers must also be mindful of sharks that prowl the waters, including huge great white sharks.

Big wave surfers understand that bigger waves mean bigger danger. They do all they can to stay safe while they chase the world's most famous monster waves.

How much higher can surfers go? No one is sure. But there's little doubt that the world's greatest surfers will continue to put their lives on the line to ride the world's biggest waves.

BRIEF BIOGRAPHIES

LAIRD HAMILTON

Many surfers consider the American Laird Hamilton the greatest big wave surfer of all time. Laird was first exposed to surfing when he was a boy on holiday with his mother in Hawaii. There, he met famous surfer Billy Hamilton, who taught him how to surf. Laird's mother eventually married Billy, who adopted Laird and became his father.

It was just the beginning of Hamilton's love of surfing. Hamilton became famous for chasing big waves. And he was one of the surfers who invented tow-in surfing, allowing him to ride ever bigger waves.

ANDREA MOLLER

Andrea Moller was born in Brazil in 1979. She moved to the
Hawaiian island of Maui in 1998 to focus on surfing. She never
left. Moller quickly became one of the best big wave surfers
on Maui. She was the first woman to do a tow-in surf on the
monster waves of Peahi, also called Jaws. Then in 2016, she
caught a 13-metre monster wave at Peahi, a record for a female
surfer. Moller did it, but it was a rough ride. A hard wipeout at
the end of her run left her with a serious leg injury.

Garrett McNamara is a big wave legend. He was born on 10 August 1967, in Pittsfield, Massachusetts, USA. McNamara discovered surfing at the age of eleven when his family moved to Hawaii. By the time he was 17, he was competing in the Hawaiian Triple Crown Series. McNamara became famous for surfing giant waves. In 2011, he set a world record by riding a 23.77-metre monster wave at Praia do Norte, Portugal. Two years later, he caught a wave estimated to be 30 metres tall!

OTHER PATHS TO EXPLORE

1. Surfers in ancient Polynesia didn't have the high-tech surfing gear of today. They used simple wooden boards and no gear. Imagine you were a surfer during these times. What kind of dangers would you experience that modern surfers wouldn't?

2. Several famous big wave surfers have died trying to surf monster waves. What kinds of precautions do surfers take to keep themselves safe in big waves?

3. This book looks at three famous monster-wave locations. But there are many others around the world. Look up other famous wave spots. Which one would you try if you were a big wave surfer?

GLOSSARY

bail out abandon one's surfboard before being wiped out by the wave

barrel tube-shaped part or curl of the wave

break when the top of a wave begins to curl and crash down in front of the rest of the wave

carve lean on a surfboard so only its edge touches the water

CPR short for cardiopulmonary resuscitation; CPR is a way of restarting a heart that has stopped beating

crest top of a wave

kick out controlled exit from a wave by riding up and over the top of the wave

leash cord used to keep the surfboard from being washed away from the surfer; surfboard leashes usually attach at the surfer's ankle

reef underwater strip of rocks, coral or sand near the surface of the ocean

short board surfboard that is about 1.8 metres (6 feet) long

swell large wave with a long, continuous crest

whitewater frothy, broken wave

FIND OUT MORE

BOOKS

Extreme Water Sports (Sports to the Extreme), Erin K. Butler (Raintree, 2018)

Surfing and Other Extreme Water Sports (Natural Thrills), Drew Lyon (Raintree, 2021)

WEBSITES

www.surfingengland.org/surf-safe/
Find out about safety tips to keep you safe when you're out on the waves.

www.worldsurfleague.com/
Check out the World Surf League website for inspiration.

INDEX